The definition of the word achievement is in dire need o

There was a time when it referred to a feat forged in va...
dedication, staying power, guts and application. Now it can be attained by simply
leaving an algorithm to run on its own, with the final results broadcast to a
potentially vast audience.

In short, it is now possible to harvest achievements as background processes while
you get on with the important tasks at hand. Namely, downloading third-party
apps that allow you to achieve even more. A global effort to recycle will soon
be undermined by the sheer length of our collective CVs.

Why, only this morning I learnt how to summon a Draenei Tomb Guardian, a
mere twenty minutes after becoming a member of the Portal Preservation
Society. I could have got it down to ten if it hadn't been for the insistent banging
at the door. Bailiffs can be so intrusive. You think they would have been impressed.

Anyway, I should dash. I've got about an hour to get to the Housing Association
Office to see if I can pay this month's rent in artichokes. If not I may have to
start selling off some of my offworld terraforming bases. Hard times.

Despite the austerity, here's the second Facebook Comicbook. Hope you enjoy
reading it as much as I enjoyed unlocking my first Completed Sequel achievement.

Paul Stapleton
beat_bedsit@yahoo.co.uk / www.pogscribbles.org

This book is in no way affiliated with or endorsed by the makers of Facebook.

Grammar Nazi

I waited forty five minutes for you – AGAIN!!! – were did you get to? i'm getting

really sick and tired of wasting my whole weekend's outside Wilkinson's waiting

for you to make an appearance. maybe if you had some idea of what a working

IT'S A HISTORICAL LANDMARK TOO, BECAUSE IT WAS THE FIRST ELECTION WHERE NOBODY GOT WHAT THEY VOTED FOR.

YEAH, BUT ANYONE WHO VOTED TORY WAS PROBABLY PRETTY HAPPY WITH THE RESULT.

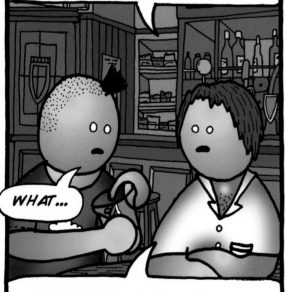

I DON'T KNOW WHAT PISSES ME OFF THE MOST THOUGH...

WHAT...

HOW THE TORIES USED THIS DEFICIT AS AN EXCUSE TO DO WHAT THEY WANTED ALL ALONG,

OR THE WAY THE LIBERALS ROLLED OVER AND *LET* THEM.

...THE HELL IS *THAT*?!

I'M TEMPTED TO TELL ANY OF MY FRIENDS WHO VOTED EITHER OF THEM TO FUCK RIGHT OFF.

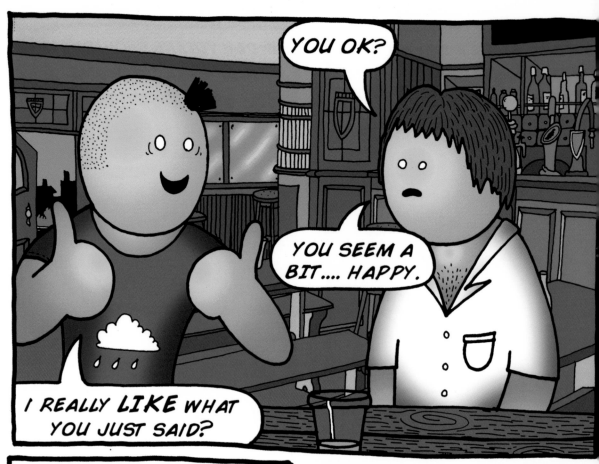

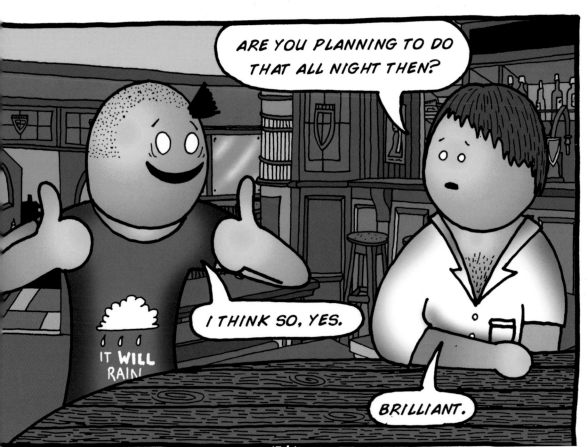

TO BE CONTINUED...

Achievements: Frontierville

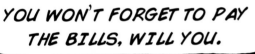

Grammar Nazi

Hey snoogums, just wanted to remind you that your the most considerate,

sexy and sweet boy I know and I know I get mental with you and im sorry.

it's my biological clock and I get a bit serious about the whole baby thing

and my periods have been a lot heavier recently. but I will make it up to you
SUPER WET
tonight ;-) xx love you love you xx
SUPER WET
SHARE.
KABOOM
YOUR' IS A POSSESSIVE ADJECTIVE, AND 'I'M' HAS AN APOSTROPHE.
I...I WAS IN A RUSH!
AND IN FUTURE, **TRY** TO DIFFERENTIATE BETWEEN A WALL POSTING AND A PRIVATE MESSAGE. I ALMOST LOST MY BREAKFAST.

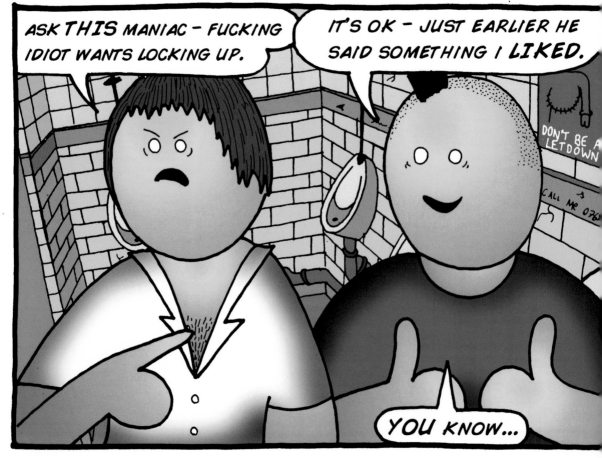

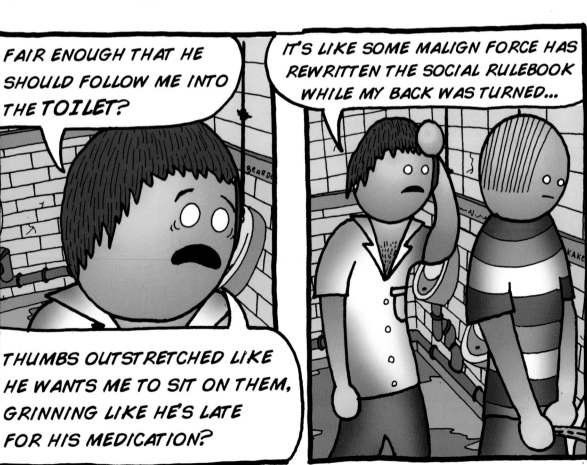

TO BE CONTINUED...

I'VE GOT $56, 561, 381, 125 IN A NEW YORK BANK,

51 MAFIA MEMBERS,

269 ATTACK POINTS,

FOR GOD'S SAKE — I'VE EVEN OPENED ACCOUNTS IN ITALY, BANGKOK, CUBA AND MOSCOW!

DESPITE THIS, EVERY NIGHT IS SPENT ALONE,

FREEZING IN MY DAMP, SQUALID BEDSIT.

FRANTICALLY DROWNING ENDLESS DORITOS IN ANYTHING I CAN FIND THAT'S RUNNIER THAN DORITOS,

WATCHING JUDGE JOHN DEED.

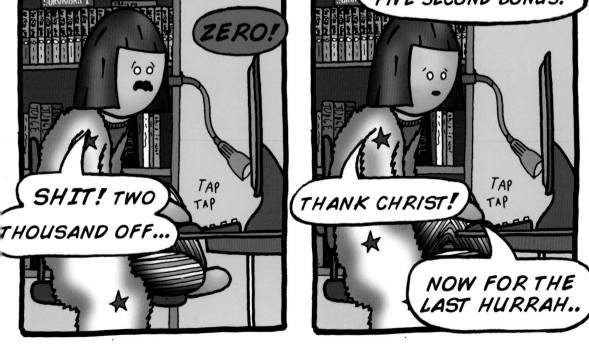

THE END.

Your "CUT OUT AND LOSE" Guide to facebook fools

I don't imagine for a minute there's anyone who is so new to social networking that they need a crash course in the defective and the inane.

However, I believe forewarned is forearmed. With that in mind, here are some pointers towards those who should be quietly ignored...

CONSTANT STREAMER

PROFILE PIC:
An out-of-focus snapshot taken and uploaded with a mobile device which is linked directly to their twitter, flickr, tumblr and blogspot accounts. Updated every eight minutes and so resembling a very primitive webcam.

LIKELY STATUS UPDATES:
* "Just leaving my house."
* "Getting on the bus now."
* "Going to work for the day. Roll on Saturday!"
* "Going to the pub to meet <insert tagged names>"
* "Could be a late one methinks!"
* "Got home. Been burgled."

FRIENDS WITH:
Prefers to think of them as 'subscribers'. but mostly people who have blocked them from their live feeds.

HOBBIES/INTERESTS:
Going to <tagged location> for <tagged event> with <tagged friend>, <tagged friend> and <tagged friend>

SWORN FACEBOOK ENEMIES:
Casual users. The sort of person who still somehow manages to combine social networking with a veneer of dignity and privacy. Clearly they're all still living in the age of the manual page refresh.

ENDLESS WELL OF ISSUES

PROFILE PIC:
A Celtic Knot, anything that references Shakti or Chi, Glastonbury Tor, a dolphin, yoga in the setting sun, a grammatically dubious and scientifically unsound piece of quasi-religious text, Nick Drake.

LIKELY STATUS UPDATES:
* "I'm so sorry I haven't updated my status for a few days - life has been an uphill struggle for me. Again."
* "In~spirilling into my soul's purpose ... I am that I am and i am happy to be just 'that'. Boomshanka."
* "I can't believe I never realised before, but I just found out that it really IS all about me!"

FRIENDS WITH:
The pathologically sympathetic, several self-help groups and a Buddhist retreat in cornwall.

HOBBIES/INTERESTS:
Baggy sleeves, vague references to unspecified self-harm, paddling in the pool of commercial spiritualism.

SWORN FACEBOOK ENEMIES:
Anyone who uses phrases like "pull your socks up", "there's plenty worse off than yourself" and "the world doesn't owe you a living". Don't they realise everything bad that can happen has happened to YOU?

BABY BORE

PROFILE PIC:
A protoplasmic blob that resembles someone having sneezed onto a blackboard. This is followed by a two year-long series of almost identical snapshots of a surly lumpen infant doing nothing of interest until the process begins again. And again.

LIKELY STATUS UPDATES:
* "My little miracle did his first bum burp this morning. I'm the happiest mummy alive."
* "My little bundle slept straight through for EIGHT HOURS! I'm a contented daddy. ZZZZZZ!!!"
* "Is it just me, or is my baby actually BETTER than everybody else's?"

FRIENDS WITH:
Other mums (even though they're all doing something wrong, clearly), local childrens' activity groups, babysitters and people they found intolerable up until the moment they too had a baby.

HOBBIES/INTERESTS:
Their baby, its development and all data pertaining to it, recalibrating moral outrage parameters.

SWORN FACEBOOK ENEMIES:
People who still attend events.

DESKTOP ACTIVIST

PROFILE PIC:
Because they're a known enemy of the state and a confirmed subversive, they throw the authorities off the scent with a stream of red and black logos and the occasional photo of Karl Marx or Che Guavara.

LIKELY STATUS UPDATES:
* "(via Twitter) It's all fucking kicking off big time at the anti-cuts demo. I've just seen it on Yahoo news."
* "If you don't sign this petition forwarded by a comrade then basically you're no better than the Nazis."
* "If vegans think they're so fucking great they clearly can't hear the carrots as they scream their last."

FRIENDS WITH:
ndymedia, once the request has been accepted.

HOBBIES/INTERESTS:
Denouncing anyone who doesn't agree with them as a fascist, denouncing the political apathy of the nation, never getting round to attending a demo.

SWORN FACEBOOK ENEMIES:
Facebook itself because it's fascistic and corporate, but they daren't delete their account because it might put them on the radar "for the fucking pigs".

SICKLY LOVER

PROFILE PIC:
A frequently updated montage of "happy couple" snaps, slowly giving the impression that this person is not an individual life form but rather part of a gestalt entity and incapable of independent motivation. Which is pretty much the case.

LIKELY STATUS UPDATES:
* "Had a wonderful day with my beautiful <tagged by name>. Can such bliss really be eternal?"
* "It's been sixteen happy weeks since we first met. Happy sort-of anniversary my sweetness xxxxxxx"
* "Has just been kindly told by my thoughful lover that I'm getting 'clingy' and 'demanding'! WTF?!?!"

FRIENDS WITH:
Their partner's friends.

HOBBIES/INTERESTS:
Their partners hobbies and interests. Even ones that include eight-sided dice, shopping incessantly both on and offline, and swinging.

SWORN FACEBOOK ENEMIES:
Their partner's ex who still wishes them a happy birthday.

WILL EVENTUALLY BECOME:
The endless well of issues.

TIRELESS FUNDRAISER

PROFILE PIC:
Starving children, soup kitchens, unspeakable poverty and all sorts of gruesome images that make you realise you could be doing something far better than levelling up on Pyramidville. Fortunately, they've embedded a 'donate' button.

LIKELY STATUS UPDATES:
* "Managed to finish the Save The Children Fun Run! 36k through the Downs - just warming up!"
* "Just think - in the time it took you to play Bejewelled Blitz, fifteen stray dogs were stabbed and eaten."
* "I'm not one of those types that says 'every little helps' - think of that when you sponsor me."

FRIENDS WITH:
The mayor, the local newspaper, every charity within a thirty mile radius and a few supermarkets.

HOBBIES/INTERESTS:
Feeling the burn, seeing the childrens' faces when their cheque is presented to the local asthma ward.

SWORN FACEBOOK ENEMIES:
People who start groups to raise awareness about major charities having either dodgy budgetary credentials, links to vivisection, or getting their merchandise made in third world sweatshops.

PUBLIC GAMER

PROFILE PIC:
A Nintendo NES controller, the Atari logo, Mario, Pac Man, a Tetris block, the Master Chief, the Commodore 64 logo. Anything to avoid revealing themselves as the pasty, crusty faced, sunken eyed hobgoblins they really are.

LIKELY STATUS UPDATES:
* "Wii emulator on my PC looks about 100x better than on a console! Fuck you Nintendo! (love you really)."
* "Gonna be on [AR51] 24/7 Crossfire #1 By WWW.TEAM-AREA51.NET pretty much all day."
* "Just heard something about GIRLS. What is GIRLS? - will it run on an NVIDIA Quadro 600 96-core CUDA?"

FRIENDS WITH:
kdeth177, wowpwner2011, black_mesa_forever, gladosisdead99, zerg_slayer, their parents.

HOBBIES/INTERESTS:
pwnage of n00bs, creating user content but never actually finishing it, watching E3 footage at 4am.

SWORN FACEBOOK ENEMIES:
Outdoor types. If God had meant us to leave the house then he wouldn't have given us World of Warcraft or Bethesda Softworks.

Grammar Nazi

its the ethnic minorities, gays and lesbians complainin gagain! All true brits

should brig back national service. next well have pedofiles teaching our

kids ho w to swmi!?! wake up people! stand up and bec ounted. what next?

THE END.

I AM A LEVEL 142 DIRECTOR OF 650 LAW FIRMS.

EACH OF THESE EARNS ME 200,000 UNITS OF BLOOD AN HOUR.

JUST THINK...

BY THE TIME THIS FILM FINISHES, I WILL HAVE GAINED 195 MILLION UNITS.

THAT'S AMOST THE EQUIVALENT OF TWENTY FIVE MILLION MEN AND WOMEN.

SO TO CELEBRATE THIS,

I'M WEARING MY BEST VELVET BOW BIT (WHICH LOOKS PERFECTLY SPLENDID),

AND A SILK CUMMERBUND.

Privacy Settings

WE CAN INTRODUCE IT AS AN OPTIONAL COMPONENT.

NOBODY LIKES OBSOLESCENCE.

FOLLOW IT WITH SOME HIGH PROFILE PRESS TO DENOUNCE ANYONE WHO HASN'T INSTALLED IT AS A SECURITY RISK,

AND A LOCKOUT WHICH BARS INTERACTION WITH ANYONE WHO HAS.

HEY - HOW ABOUT A POP-DOWN MENU WHICH LIMITS STATUS UPDATES TO SYNTAX TEMPLATES!

WE CAN MARKET IT AS A TIME-SAVING FEATURE!

TIME SAVING? HA!

WITH *OUR* USER BASE, THAT WOULD BE LIKE OFFERING A MONEY-SAVING SCHEME TO *MILLIONAIRES*.

JEFFREY **WILL** HAVE HIS LADIES.

EVEN IF HE HAS TO CODE NIGHT AND DAY WITHOUT AIR OR FOOD.

JEFFREY **WILL. NOT. BE. ALONE.**

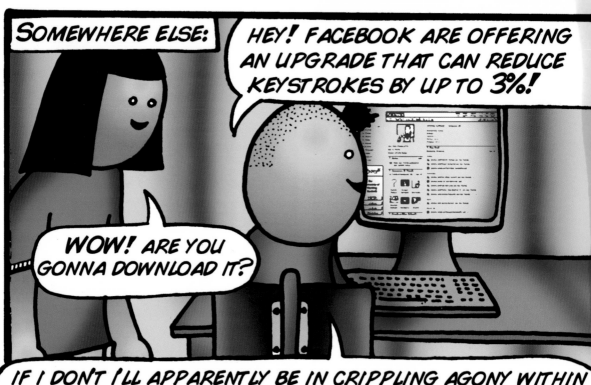

SOMEWHERE ELSE:

HEY! FACEBOOK ARE OFFERING AN UPGRADE THAT CAN REDUCE KEYSTROKES BY UP TO **3%**!

WOW! ARE YOU GONNA DOWNLOAD IT?

IF I DON'T I'LL APPARENTLY BE IN CRIPPLING AGONY WITHIN A MONTH, AND **YOU'LL** RUN OFF WITH SOMEONE ON OUR MUTUAL FRIENDS LIST. I RECKON I MAY AS WELL!